WRITTEN BY
Katie Cook

ART BY
Andy Price

COLORS BY
Heather Breckel

LETTERS BY
Robbie Robbins

EDITED BY
Bobby Curnow

COVER BY
Stephanie Buscema

DIGEST EDITS BY
Justin Eisinger & Alonzo Simon

DIGEST DESIGN BY
Neil Uyetake

For Grayson, my own lil' Cutie Mark Crusader. –Katie

With great love to friends and family, for my wife Alice and our cats Spooky, Tabitha,
Boris, Bela, and Mina. And above all, especially for Sam —Andy

Special thanks to Erin Comella, Robert Fewkes, Heather Hopkins, Valerie Jurries, Ed Lane, Brian Lenard, Marissa Mansolillo, Donna Tobin, Michael Vogel, Mark Wiesenhahn, and Michael Kelly for their invaluable assistance.

IDW founded by Ted Adams, Alex Garner, Kris Oprisko, and Robbie Robbins

ISBN: 978-1-61377-628-5   16 15 14 13   1 2 3 4

Licensed By:

Ted Adams, CEO & Publisher
Greg Goldstein, President & COO
Robbie Robbins, EVP/Sr. Graphic Artist
Chris Ryall, Chief Creative Officer/Editor-in-Chief
Matthew Ruzicka, CPA, Chief Financial Officer
Alan Payne, VP of Sales
Dirk Wood, VP of Marketing
Lorelei Bunjes, VP of Digital Services

Become our fan on Facebook facebook.com/idwpublishing
Follow us on Twitter @idwpublishing
Check us out on YouTube youtube.com/idwpublishing
www.IDWPUBLISHING.com

TWILIGHT SPARKLE

Twilight Sparkle is a unicorn with a big heart. Even though she prefers to have her muzzle stuck in a book, she's always willing to put her work aside to help her friends! She's also one of the most magically gifted unicorns there is thanks to her studies and the personal guidance of Princess Celestia.

RARITY

Rarity is a unicorn who has dedicated her life to making beautiful things... She's a fashion designer in Ponyville and has aspirations to be "the biggest thing in Equestria." She has big dreams, but she's very dedicated to her Ponyville friends who have always been there for her.

FLUTTERSHY

Fluttershy is a shy pegasus with a gentle hoof. Her love and understanding of animals is almost legendary to the ponies around her. She's calm and collected, even when faced with some of the scariest beings in the Everfree forest!

APPLEJACK

Applejack is a pony you can trust. She's the hardest worker in all of Ponyville and will always be there to lend a helping hoof! She and her family run Sweet Apple Acres, the foremost place to acquire apples and apple-related goodies in Ponyville.

PINKIE PIE

Pinkie Pie is a pony that likes to PAR-TAY. Friendly, funny... and maybe a little weird, Pinkie Pie is always on hoof for a celebration for any occasion! She's always there with a smile and an elaborate cake, even if she's just saying "thanks for pet-sitting my alligator."

RAINBOW DASH

Rainbow Dash is the fastest pegasus around... and she KNOWS it! Never one to turn down a challenge, she's always ready to seize the day (in the spirit of friendly competition of course!).

SPIKE

Spike the Dragon is the pint-sized assistant to Twilight Sparkle. Besides helping her out in the Ponyville library, he helps her practice spells and the duties of her daily life... he may be in the designated role of "helper," but he's also her dear friend.

QUEEN CHRYSALIS

Queen Chrysalis is the Queen of the Changelings. After a failed attempt to take over Equestria, she now has her sights set on Twilight and her friends.

PRINCESS CELESTIA

Princess Celestia is the ruler of Equestria and Twilight Sparkle's mentor. Princess Celestia is kind, gentle, and powerful... everything she needs to be to rule and protect her kingdom.

THE CUTIE MARK CRUSADERS

The Cutie Mark Crusaders are comprised of Sweetie Belle, Apple Bloom, and Scootaloo. These young fillies have yet to earn their cutie marks (the image on a pony's flank depicting their special talent!) and they are dashing through task after task together with the sole purpose of finding what makes them unique.

THAT SOUNDS... DARK.

...AND SPOOKY.

ERR... *THROUGH* THE MOUNTAIN? LET'S JUST GO *OVER* IT.

WE CAN'T ALL *FLY*, RAINBOW DASH.

THE FASTEST WAY IS *THROUGH* THE MOUNTAIN.

WE'VE ONLY GOT *THREE DAYS* TO SAVE SWEETIE BELLE, APPLEBLOOM, AND SCOOTALOO. I SAY WE TAKE THE FASTEST ROUTE.

WELL, FOR *ME*, THE FASTEST ROUTE IS OVER THE MOUNTAIN.

NO. WE STAY TOGETHER AS A GROUP.

LET'S GET THIS PARTY STARTED!

THIS ISN'T A PARTY, PINKIE, IT'S A RESCUE MISSION!

YOU KNOW WHAT I MEAN.

DO WE KNOW WHERE THE ENTRANCE TO THE MINE IS?

I'M SURE I CAN FIND IT... IF THEY MINED GEMS, I KNOW I'LL BE ABLE TO SENSE IT!

UH... I DON'T THINK WE'LL NEED YOUR SUPER-GEM SENSES TO TELL US WHERE IT IS...

...EEK!

WELL, WE'RE NOT MAKING ANY PROGRESS IF WE'RE STANDIN' HERE GAWKIN'. LET'S MOVE!

...EEEEEEEEEK!

I WONDER HOW LONG IT'S BEEN SINCE ANYONE MINED THESE CAVES? THE GEMS LOOK TO BE LONG GONE... DISAPPOINTING, REALLY. ALL THAT'S LEFT IS BORING OLD ROCKS.

BORING OLD ROCKS AND *THIS GUY!* SAY "HI" TO MR. BONES!

"'ELLO PINKIE!"

RUMBLE

WELL, HOPEFULLY THAT MEANS NO ONE IS HERE AND WE CAN JUST WALK ON THROUGH WITH NO ISSUES!

PFFT... SAYING THINGS LIKE THAT JUST MEANS YOU'RE *BEGGING* FOR SOMETHING TO HAPPEN.

SEE?

PO-NAYS?